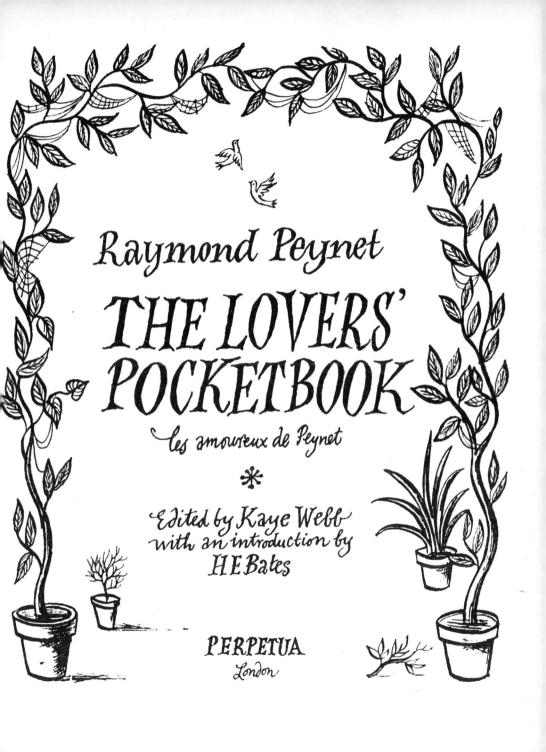

Raymond Peynet

THE LOVERS' POCKETBOOK

les amoureux de Peynet

✳

Edited by Kaye Webb
with an introduction by
H E Bates

PERPETUA
London

First Published by
PERPETUA LTD.,
32 Newton Road,
London, W.2,
and distributed for them by
MICHAEL JOSEPH LTD.,
26 Bloomsbury Street,
London, W.C.1.
SEPTEMBER 1954
SECOND IMPRESSION SEPTEMBER 1954
THIRD IMPRESSION NOVEMBER 1954
FOURTH IMPRESSION DECEMBER 1955
FIFTH IMPRESSION MARCH 1956
SIXTH IMPRESSION DECEMBER 1956

Set and printed in Great Britain by The Hollen Street Press Ltd
London W1.

Introduction

The past year has provided two endearing works of art, both French, that seem to me to have much the same quality of delicious and inconsequential charm. One is Jacques Tati's film *M. Hulot's Holiday*, that droll piece of poetry in mime that tells us all we ever need to know, as in a hilarious dream, about a holiday at the coast of Northern France. The other is *Les Amoureux de Peynet*.

Our age is an anxious one. It has been, artistically, a bony, steely, wiry, unbending time, in which the application of the word charm to a work of art has been tantamount to damning it in all serious eyes for ever. Music similarly has been miserably afraid to enchant us; literature, with the world and the war on its conscience, has been terrified of happiness and the candid attempt to make us laugh. We have been prone to make a fetish of plays with buried spiritual meanings and have been fed—I now suggest to the teeth—with films and literature in which no act or word, however gross, is spared.

We sorely need a change from this, and it is largely the graphic artists, not always necessarily cartoonists, who have done something towards providing it. Osbert Lancaster, Emett, and

Ronald Searle have not been afraid of joy; and Peynet, the most joyous of them all, has not been afraid of the sin of being sentimental.

Peynet was born in 1908, and in the years before the war was already contributing caricatures to *Le Rire, France Dimanche, Ici Paris,* and other French newspapers. It was, however, not until after the war, in our still grimmer age of anxiety, that he evolved *Les Amoureux,* his intimate and inimitable lovers. They are undoubtedly the nicest lovers in the world.

Where else in the world is there a girl who knits perfect love while her lover holds her wool in the shape of a heart? Where else does the hurdy-gurdy provide beds—and oh! such French ones!—instead of rocket ships and racing cars? Where else does a girl's underwear unravel itself in the form of railway trains or provide a muff for hands grown cold in winter parks? Where else do the tears of love make garlands, and the garlands of autumn make tresses of hair? And where else, pray, does the *soutien-gorge* provide proud biceps for an adoring husband? Nowhere, of course, except in Peynet.

A glance at these pages will at once convince the reader that no introduction to Peynet would possibly be complete without some further reference to his tenderest *motif.* His lovers have been described as "still half in their childhood, for ever astonished by the sight of the world and by their love"; the girl, *La Fiancée* has been called a "candid little girl who has lost her virtue without quite understanding how." She and her poet love, with his long hair, stiff collar and bowler hat, live in an allegorical world in which all objects are theirs for amorous manipulation and where the bosom is the crowning means of love's delight.

Just as the lovers themselves are quite the nicest lovers in the world, so are these the nicest bosoms. Is there anything nicer than the scene of tender detachment on the park seat, when a lover nurses the apples of his delight?

These objects, like some other parts of *La Fiancée's* enchanting anatomy, are constantly being revealed for us with grave and tender delight. The heart is similarly laid bare for us and sometimes, since love is poor, is also seen to be weeping and made of gold. Music comes out of the tops of her stockings. Confiture of cherries hangs from her ears. Poverty takes away the seat of her skirt but never her dignity. All this, let it be emphasised, is in perfect taste.

Poets, as our heroine remarks, are not as other men, even though they ought to realise that midnight is a reasonable enough hour to come to bed. And Peynet, without doubt is a poet. His world of lovers, of parks, of birds, of cherrytime, of daisy-chains, and daisy clocks, of harps that are prisons and bosoms that are symbols is intensely lyrical. It is also intensely French. We in England have nothing like it—or at least we hadn't until, thank Heaven and Kaye Webb, this incomparable book appeared.

H. E. BATES

"Spring-a-ling-aling! Spring-a-ling-aling!"

Heart to Heart

"*Nobody can be as much in love as we are.*"
"*That's what you think, look at those two!*"

"*I'm a fishmonger.*"
"*And I'm a typist in a flower shop.*"

"Eight-fifteen already; how time flies . . ."

Lover's Reckoning

"Would someone please press the button? Thank you!"

Spring Song

"She loves me, she loves me not, she loves me . . ."

"These fairy stories quite carry me away, darling!"

"No, you choose."

"How dare you—dress me at once.'"

"My hands get cold . . ."

"Oh why did you do it when I loved you so?"

"Chocolates! Cigarettes!—Anti-freeze!"

"You're homesick—I can see it in your eyes!"

"Toys—that way, Sir!"

". . . and I've two delightful little knick-knacks just inside, if you would care to see them."

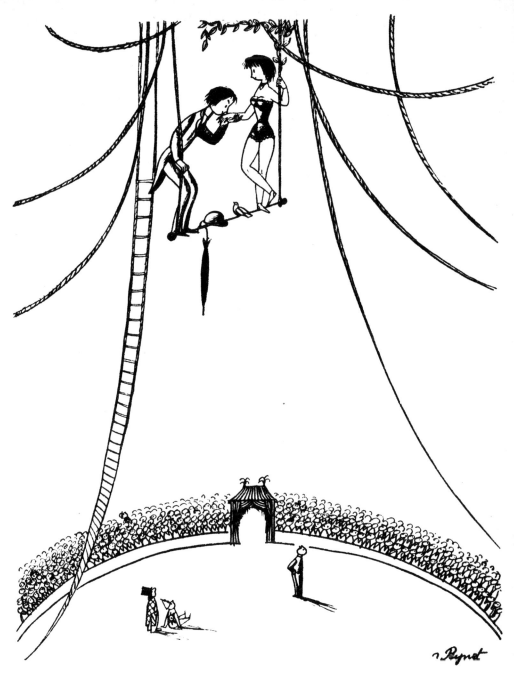

"I was passing by and I thought I'd drop in . . ."

"Huh! Is she afraid someone will steal him?"

"*How would you like it; half in hearts of gold
and the rest in billets doux?*"

"What, jam-making already!"

1. Peynet

"A-lou-ette, gentille a-lou-et-te . . ."

"And he has the cheek to say it's all his own work!"

"*Mi, mi, la, sol, si, fa, re . . .*"

"Don't mind Mummy—-she's a bit old-fashioned."

"I couldn't wait, so I came to meet you!"

"Oh, darling! Listen how my heart is beating!"

"It can't be very gay for you—living all alone in a forest!"

"You make me feel I can trust you . . ."

'*My name's Kathleen—K for Kingfisher, A for Avocet, T for Turtle Dove . . .*'

"I've a little bit tucked away which will help us to be happy!"

"Oh dear, have I kept you waiting?"

"There—I wasn't long, was I?"

La Ronde

*". . . and we'll have geraniums in the windows and a
little cat on the roof . . ."*

"Oh, darling—a little place of our own at last!"

"It's like that every evening . . . dreaming at their window . . ."

"Jacques a weakling?—You should see his muscles!"

"I know, Mama . . . I <u>expected</u> a poet to be different but . . ."

*"Yes, sweetheart, I'll save you from your dreadful dream
—if you'll tell me where you put the key . . ."*

"Still cross, dearest?"

"Any one would think the neighbours were <u>interested</u> in our troubles!"

"Beloved! I've been so worried!"

"*Silly to part for ever, just for a tiff.*"

Un Cœur d'Or

WEATHER FORECAST

"Showers of kisses with local heart storms. The sky will turn rosy towards evening. Swallows will fly low and the night will fall softly . . ."

This is the first Peynet book to be published in this country, although his cartoons have illumined the pages of one of our monthly magazines and his first drawing to be published, when he was 22, appeared in *The Boulvardier,* a magazine for English residents in Paris.

This November he will be 46, but the years have lain lightly. Peynet lovers are taller, more elegant, nowadays; Peynet ladies more enticing, their misfortunes more touching, their delights more entrancing. M. Peynet himself has matured romantically; Mme. Denise Peynet, whose gamin features are recognisable in every drawing, has rounded out.

They still live in Paris, M. Peynet's hometown (where they were art students together) but now they have a black-haired daughter Annie. The front room of their flat is inhabited by life-sized models of The Poet and His Fiancée, *Elle et Lui,* as M. Peynet habitually calls them, and is otherwise full of delicate conceits:  Peynet could flourish as an interior decorator any time he chose. Now the Peynets also have a picturesque ruin in Biot lovingly restored to domesticity and suitably smothered in orange blossom!

Today Peynet is one of the most famous of French cartoonists. His work won the Grand Prix at an International Festival of Humour, his illustrated books, his ballet and theatre décors, his posters and window designs enchant Parisians, from Spring to Winter.

Colette Vasselon has written of him: "In these drawings we rediscover the emotions of growing youth, of our earliest love, and our first tryst; and we realise how deep is the philosophy of this naïve and simple life. Houses are there to shelter men and their happiness, flowers to charm their eyes, animals to love them and serve them . . . Even sorrows and disillusionment are here on a scale made to fit man himself; hate being shut out . . ."

If you ask Peynet if he truly sees life in this '*humour rose*' he answers, "*Je sais que ce n'est pas la même chose partout mais . . .*" and dark-eyed Denise, her eyes glinting with memories of battles won before they were fought, adds "*Raymond est très pacifique.*"

Paris loves him, Europe has acclaimed him, now we believe Great Britain will make a complete surrender to his innocence and gaiety. K.W.

PERPETUA   BOOKS

CHRISTOPHER FRY
An Experience of Critics

★

Edited by KAYE WEBB Illustrated by RONALD SEARLE
Prologue by ALEC GUINNESS with notes on the
APPROACH TO DRAMATIC CRITICISM by eight distinguished critics.
'Dramatic critics and their victims brought together in a highly entertaining experiment
. . . commended to all theatre lovers with or without greasepaint . . .'   PUNCH
'Elegantly produced and urbanely written . . .'   THE TIMES LITERARY SUPPLEMENT
Crown 8vo 7/6 net (Fourth Impression)

RONALD SEARLE
Souls in Torment

★

'There may, for all I know, be those who are less than enthusiastic about Ronald
Searle's work, but to addicts like myself they are incomprehensible.'
MALCOLM MUGGERIDGE in *Punch*

'A draughtsmanship at once delicate and boldly architectural, a wit subtle, high-spirited,
masculine and schizophrenic—it is this combination which provides Mr Ronald Searle
with his shattering effects and makes him unique among British cartoonists . . .   Mr
Searle's is the wit of his age.'   J. D. SCOTT in *The Spectator*

'Humour of this sort is neither topical in subject nor modish in style. It is timeless and
universal . . . Collectors are therefore recommended to purchase rather than to borrow
this book.'   ERIC NEWTON in *Time and Tide*

Crown 4to, 12/6 net (Fourth Impression)

PUBLISHED BY PERPETUA LTD. 32 NEWTON ROAD W2 AND DISTRIBUTED
BY MICHAEL JOSEPH LIMITED 26 BLOOMSBURY STREET WC1